JOYCE HUGGETT

*

PRAYER JOURNAL

Marshall Pickering
An Imprint of HarperCollins*Publishers*

Marshall Pickering is an Imprint of
HarperCollins*Religious*
Part of HarperCollins*Publishers*
77-85 Fulham Palace Road, London W6 8JB

First published in Great Britain
in 1990 by Marshall Morgan and Scott,
a forerunner of Marshall Pickering

3 5 7 9 10 8 6 4

A catalogue record for this book is
available from the British Library

0 551 01950-6

Printed and bound in Great Britain by
Hartnolls Ltd, Bodmin, Cornwall

For Henry and the household at Launde Abbey
with so many thanks

As always, a whole variety of people have helped to bring this book into being. Here, I would like to thank just a handful.

First, my thanks go to Gerard Hughes SJ *who, more than anyone, helped me to discover the way of praying which I describe in this book. I would also like to thank publicly Isobel Gregory, who read the original manuscript, gave me the encouragement I needed and suggested various changes which I valued.*

Third, I must make mention of Christine Whitell, the editor who first sowed in my mind the seed-thought from which this Prayer Journal grew. Without the help of Linda Cooper my time to keep a Prayer Journal and to write books would be severely limited and I am more grateful to her for her hidden ministry than I can say.

And my final vote of thanks goes to the Rev John Harding, whose illustrations bring to life many of the wise words about prayer which I have quoted. Over the years John's ministry has touched the lives of various members of my family and I was delighted when he agreed to work with me on this project. I have appreciated not only his sensitive illustrations but his constructive, creative interest in the book.

Contents

Keeping A Prayer Journal

'Ducking under'. That is the term one friend of mine uses to describe the Quiet Days I carve out of my diary each month: days when I leave my work and retreat, wherever possible, to a quiet Convent or cottage to be still, to reflect, to meditate and to pray.

At first this term amused me. But one day the phrase took on a new significance.

I was standing beside the pond at a certain Retreat House I frequent. An all-brown duck was swimming solo across the unruffled surface of the water. But every so often, as though to entertain me, he would stop swimming, turn a quick somersault and disappear under the water.

What impressed me most was not my feathered friend's acrobatics but the effect his antics had on the water. Every time the little tufted head penetrated the pond, rings would spread in ever-widening circles from his diving spot right across the pool.

'That's what happens when people pray', God seemed to say. 'Not one single droplet of the pool of the world remains untouched.'

This simple, but profound, reminder of the power of prayer moved me deeply. It moves me still when I recall it. So much so that I have in my Prayer Journal a sketch of that particular pond – and the performing duck.

'My Prayer Journal.' It is because I believe in this mysterious, divine energy called prayer that, for the past fifteen years, I have kept a prayer journal. For most of that time I have used an ordinary spiral-bound notebook. In it I have written letters to God in which I have expressed my joy and my pain, my excitement and my anger, my disappointments and my hopes – everything that really matters to me. In it, too, I have recorded God's 'letters' to me: the messages he seems to have been anxious to underline from his revealed Word, the Bible – or through sermons and talks, books and articles, pictures and prophecies, nature and dreams.

For years I have been content to pour out my innermost feelings to God in this way. But recently the realisation has dawned that a

Prayer Journal which has a certain structure can be an even more effective aid to prayer. I say this because as I look back on some of my letters to God, I recognise that it is all too easy to write one letter of complaint after another and to omit to thank God for his over-flowing generosity. It is also possible to become so absorbed in pouring out personal pain that the pressing problems overwhelming others and our world are overlooked and omitted from our prayer.

No sooner had I determined to change my style of journalling than I found, in an obscure bookshop, a notebook which was divided into four sections. Seeing its potential, I bought it and labelled the first section **Thanksgiving**, the second **Recollection**, the third **Requests** and the fourth **Reflections**. In that it restored a healthy objectivity, it revolutionised my prayer life so I made a similar one for my husband, writing on each page a verse of Scripture and a quotation about prayer which stimulated, challenged or encouraged me. Unaccustomed though he was to keeping a Prayer Journal, David grew to value this method of praying too.

And we discovered an unexpected bonus. Writing regularly in our prayer journal not only helped us as individuals but as a partnership also. Because we had recorded reasons why we were grateful to God or ways in which God seemed to be challenging us to change, it became easier to share with one another the substance of our prayer and, inevitably, this brought about a deepening of our spiritual bonding.

From these crude beginnings this Prayer Journal eventually emerged and I am particularly excited by it because I sense its potential not only for people like me who **can** carve out chunks of the day for concentrated prayer but for young mums with clamouring children, commuters, nurses, policemen and others doing shift work – for anyone who really wants to pray. All it needs is between ten and fifteen minutes each day. It is my prayer as the book goes to print that people of all walks of life will use it and be as encouraged in their prayer pilgrimage as David and I have been.

Joyce Huggett
August 1989

John Harding
1989

Giving Thanks

I have reserved this first section of the journal for recording snippets of praise because although the Psalmist exhorts us to 'come before him with thanksgiving', many of us find it easier to come into God's presence with grumbles and groans, complaints and requests rather than with gratitude.

Different people will use this section in different ways and at different times. But I would like to recommend the method of using it which I find of greatest value. Every day, I set aside five minutes when I tune into God's presence and during which, with God, I watch an action re-play of the previous twenty-four hours, bringing into sharp focus only those moments which have been pleasurable for some reason. When I have recalled such moments, I savour them afresh, relish them and then record them in my journal in the form of words or phrases, pictures or sketches which capture the joy: 'Tadpoles, the magnificent walk, the welcome we received in the restaurant, another good nignt's sleep, the variegated greens of the countryside, the beckoning beach with its turquoise sea, church bells summoning worshippers to church. For these and all your mercies, I praise you dearest Lord,' I wrote on one occasion.

'And what happens when you've had a lousy day?' someone once asked me when I was recommending this practice at one of my Prayer Schools. The more lousy the day appears to have been, the more important this discipline.

On dark days, when the future seems bleak and we feel battered and bruised, it is easy to be beguiled into believing that there is nothing for which to praise God. But that assumption is usually far from the truth. On such occasions, if we pause to look back in the way I have described, and home in on his gifts to us, we shall see that the darkness has been spangled with pin-pricks of light even though we may not have detected them when they first began to twinkle.

On one such day, I struggled to recall tiny signs of God's love and beauty. But when I paused to look back, I recalled 'the dawn chorus, time to pour out my pain to the God who cares, the kind invitation to the concert, a wonderful sunny summer's morning, the hedgehogs L. gave me, trees heavy with pink and white cherry blossom, a cloudless slate-blue sky'. And I was forced to admit that my seemingly dismal day had been punctuated with good gifts which were in danger of being overlaid by gloom.

Most of us can make five minutes a day if we really want to. For some, it will be before the family begins to stir, for others it will be during a quiet coffee break, while others will wait until the day is drawing to its close. When we come into God's presence with praise matters little. What does matter is that we do come. And I think I can guarantee that those who set aside a regular time to express their thanks to God will discover that every minute is time very well spent.

'Sing a new song to the Lord'

Psalm 96:1

Date:

Giving Thanks

'Let your mind drift over the day...attending to and relishing only those moments of the day for which you are grateful'

Gerard Hughes SJ ***God of Surprises***
DLT 1986 p.78

'Rejoice in the Lord always. I will say it again. Rejoice!'

Philippians 4:4

Date:

Giving Thanks

'We know our Father, so we know His secrets cannot possibly contain anything but love'

Amy Carmichael ***Fragments that Remain***
Ed. Bee Trehane Triangle 1987 p.146

'I have more than an overweight of joy'

2 Corinthians 7:4 Conybeare's Translation

Date:

Giving Thanks

'Over again I feel thy finger and find thee'

Gerard Manley Hopkins SJ
The Wreck of the Deutschland

'Sing a new song to the Lord; he has done wonderful things!'

Psalm 98:1

Date:

Giving Thanks

'The world is charged with the presence and glory of God'

John Powell SJ ***He Touched Me***
Argus 1974 p.59

'Worship the Lord with joy; come before him with happy songs'

Psalm 100:1

Date:

Giving Thanks

'The Bible begins with creation and ends with worship. That is the direction in which we must all move'

Michael Marshall ***Renewal in Worship***
Marshall, Morgan and Scott 1982 p.21

*'And I heard every creature in heaven, on earth, and in the world below, and in the sea – all living beings in the universe – and they were singing:
"To him who sits on the throne and to the Lamb, be praise and honour, glory and might, for ever and ever!"'*

Revelation 5:13

Date:

Giving Thanks

This is what we were created for – 'to glorify God and to enjoy him for ever!'

Stephen Travis ***The Jesus Hope***
Word Books 1974 p.76

'His compassions never fail, they are new every morning; great is your faithfulness'

Lamentations 3:22,23

Date:

Giving Thanks

'Turn my seeing into loving'

Evelyn Underhill ***Meditations and Prayer***
Longman, Green and Co 1955 p.10

'Every good and perfect gift is from above, coming down from the Father...who does not change like shifting shadows'

James 1:17

Date:

Giving Thanks

'All good gifts around us are sent from heaven above; Then thank the Lord, O thank the Lord, For all his love'

Matthias Claudius tr. Montgomery Campbell

'The heavens declare the glory of God; the skies proclaim the work of his hands'

Psalm 19:1

Date:

Giving Thanks

'When we look at all that is created we are raised up to adoration of the Creator'

St Gregory the Great

'O Lord, our Lord, how majestic is your name in all the earth!'

Psalm 8.1

Date:

Giving Thanks

'God is not so much the object of our knowledge as the cause of our wonder'

Kallistos Ware ***The Orthodox Way***
Mowbrays 1979 p.16

'Love the Lord your God with all your heart and with all your soul and with all your strength and with all your mind'

Luke 10.27

Date:

Giving Thanks

'By love can he be caught and held, but by thinking never'

Cloud of Unknowing

'O Lord my God, you are very great; you are clothed with splendour and majesty'

Psalm 104.1

Date:

Giving Thanks

'Wherever we look, we see not only confusion but beauty. In snowflake, leaf or insect, we discover structured patterns of a delicacy that nothing manufactured by human skill can equal'

Kallistos Ware ***The Orthodox Way***
Mowbrays 1979 p.23

Looking Back

Just as it is easy to forget to thank God for his goodness, so it is pitifully possible to go through the motions of prayer and to remain unaware of the Holy Spirit's activity in us. That is why I have reserved this section of the journal for another opportunity to review our life.

Again, different people will use this section in different ways but again, there is one way which I would recommend because it has helped countless Christians to grow in maturity and Christlikeness.

As I explained in the introduction to the Thanksgiving section, there is value in spending some five minutes each day watching an action re-play of the past twenty-four hours and asking God to slow down the film when he wants to remind us of the good gifts he has given us. That section of the journal can be summed up in two words: THANK YOU. Similarly, this section may be summed up in the words: SHOW ME.

What we are attempting to do is to watch the action re-play for a second time, or, as I prefer to think of this second five-minute prayer period, we take a walk around the garden of our life with God as our companion and we ask him to point out where the fruit produced by his Spirit has started to bud or mature in us or, conversely, where weeds threaten to gain a stranglehold. This walk is always an adventure in the sense that we can never predict beforehand what God will point out. What we can anticipate is that sometimes the experience will be moving and at other times it will be challenging.

Sometimes it is moving because this 'God of Surprises', to borrow Gerard Hughes' phrase, shows us where, by his grace, the love, joy, peace, patience, kindness and self-control Paul mentions in Galatians 5:22 has been offered by us to others to their advantage or where we have been enabled by him to do things which, in our own strength, we would be incapable of achieving. He does this by bringing to the surface of our memory occasions when we have been uncharacteristically kind or patient or moments when what we have said or done has clearly been inspired by him, or times when he has prompted us to pray for someone just when they most needed it. Such memories are humbling and draw from us gratitude that the Spirit of Jesus continues to transform us.

At other times we may find God focusing on far less attractive, even ugly, parts of our day. Frequently, for example, he will point out a particular mood – like irritability. And I have learned that when this happens I must not confess too quickly. To do that would be like plucking the leaves off a weed rather than digging it up by its roots. No. Instead, I must ask myself, 'What was it that gave rise to the irritability?'

I remember asking this question on one occasion and discovering that my irritability stemmed from a conversation I had had with a woman who seemed to talk at me rather than to me and I had become more and more irritable and bad tempered even though I did not, I think, convey this frustration to her.

'Your attitude needs to change', God seemed to whisper. 'You still need to grow in your ability to accept and love people just as they are.' The home-truth was lovingly given and I admitted that it was all too accurate. And this resulted in repentance, not just of a few moments of impatience, but of something much deeper: the self-centredness which would keep at arm's length one of God's people who hurts so much that she feels she has to talk at people to conceal her pain.

On other occasions, the mood under scrutiny might appear to be a positive one: like euphoria. Again I have learned to look beneath the mood to the underlying attitude; to ask: 'Why was I euphoric? Was it because I was overwhelmed by the beauty of the countryside and was praising and reverencing God while I was walking? Was it because God was being glorified in some other way or his Kingdom being extended? Or was it, perhaps, because I was the centre of attention or because my ego was being boosted in some subtle way?'

The reason we ask these questions is because God has created us in such a way that we will only be truly happy when our life revolves around him. Yet deeply ingrained in each of us is a seam of selfishness which demands that our life-style has at its centre, not God, but self. And so we are caught in a constant struggle. We might make the claim with our lips: 'Jesus is Lord of my life' but when we examine our attitudes we see that the gulf between our words and our attitudes still needs to be bridged.

It is the Holy Spirit's task to pin-point these inconsistencies. And it is vital that we ask him to help us with this section of the journal. If we were left to do it on our own, many of us would quickly start to condemn ourselves. But the Holy Spirit is loving and gentle. He is, after all, the Spirit of Jesus. He has no desire to send us on a guilt trip. On the contrary, his one desire is to draw us nearer and nearer to God. If he highlights areas which need cleansing or attention it is only because he wants the garden of our life to bring pleasure to God, to others and ourselves. We need therefore to accept such revelations as moments of grace and give thanks for them.

There is a prayer I frequently pray as I begin this section of my journal. It is based on a prayer the Psalmist once prayed:

Search me, dear Lord, and show me myself
Show me if there is anything hurtful in me
Show me, too, where I am growing in grace.

'Clothe yourselves with…kindness'

Colossians 3.12

Looking Back

'After thanksgiving, the next step is to recall your inner moods and feelings noting, if you can, what occasioned them…Be with Christ as you look at these moods and beg him to show you the attitudes which underlie them…Just relive, in Christ's presence, the events which gave rise to them'

Gerard Hughes SJ ***God of Surprises***
DLT 1986 p.78

'Clothe yourselves with…patience'

Colossians 3:12

Date:

Looking Back

'Contemplate the events of the day and pray to Christ out of your experience of them. Sometimes this can be very painful...we can begin to see with clarity our own refusal to understand, listen, be compassionate or treat the other person or persons, with love'

Gerard Hughes SJ ***God of Surprises***
DLT 1986 p.78

'Clothe yourself with compassion'

Colossians 3:12

Date:

Looking Back

'Compassion asks us to go where it hurts, to enter into places of pain, to share in brokenness, fear, confusion and anguish'

Henri Nouwen ***Compassion***
DLT 1982 p.4

'Clothe yourselves with...humility'

Colossians 3:12

Date:

Looking Back

'True humility is an authentic appreciation of ourselves in a way that neither exaggerates nor underestimates what we are'

*Jack Dominian **The Capacity to Love***
DLT 1985 p.57

'Clothe yourselves with…gentleness'

Colossians 3:12

Date:

Looking Back

'Gentleness is "the ability to place oneself in another's shoes and so identify with his feelings that no needless pain is inflicted"'

Joyce Huggett ***Living Free***
IVP 1984 p.84

'Forgive as the Lord forgave you'

Colossians 3:13

Date:

Looking Back

'Let no one cry over his sins, for from the tomb has come forgiveness; let no one fear death, for the Saviour's death has saved us'

St John Chrysostom

'Do not grumble'

1 Corinthians 10:10

Date:

Looking Back

'We fall and get up, fall and get up, fall and get up again'

Tito Colliander

'Do not let any unwholesome talk come out of your mouths, but only what is helpful for building others up'

Ephesians 4:29

Date:

Looking Back

'We must learn to behave in the presence of the invisible Lord as we would in the presence of the Lord made visible to us'

Anthony Bloom ***Living Prayer***
Libra Books 1966 p.12

'When you stand praying, if you hold anything against anyone, forgive him, so that your Father in heaven may forgive you your sins'

Mark 11:25

Date:

Looking Back

'When people hurt us, we must forgive them...This is no ordinary command – it is an ultimatum'

Richard Walters ***Anger:*** *What To Do About It IVP 1981 p.74*

'Because of his great love for us, God who is rich in mercy made us alive with Christ even when we were dead in transgressions'

Ephesians 2:4

Date:

Looking Back

'Our faults are like a grain of sand beside the great mountain of the mercies of God'

St Jean-Baptiste Vianney

'Do not grieve the Holy Spirit'

Ephesians 4:30

Date:

Looking Back

'The Holy Spirit can be grieved and quenched not only by our sins and negligence, but also by our busyness and lack of loving attention'

Brother Ramon SSF ***The Hidden Fire***
Marshall Pickering 1985 p.32

'The Holy Spirit...will convict the world of guilt'

John 16:7

Date:

Looking Back

'The Holy Spirit may at any time convict us of selfishness or lack of love or anything that is not in keeping with Christianity. Act on it, confess it, get cleansed'

Michael Baughen ***The Prayer Principle***
Mowbrays 1983 p.53

'The Spirit helps us in our weakness. We do not know what we ought to pray for, but the Spirit himself intercedes for us with groans that words cannot express'

Romans 8:26

Date:

Looking Back

'The Helper's…task is to create in us…the basic desire to pray. He is the One who also spotlights for us the prayer-need or topic for prayer by creating a "concern" within us'

Catherine Marshall ***The Helper***
Hodder and Stoughton 1978 p.117

Requesting

Praying for oneself seems to be as natural as breathing. Even unbelievers confess to whispering a prayer as they settle themselves into a dentist's chair or as the aeroplane in which they are travelling takes off or lands.

Jesus makes it clear that the heavenly Father wants us to ask him for things. Just as loving, earthly parents delight in lavishing on their offspring good gifts at an appropriate time, so our heavenly Father hovers in the wings waiting for us to make our requests known to him in simple, petitionary prayers.

Jesus even encourages us to be persistent and specific when praying such prayers. Often when people came to him with requests on their lips, he would ask them the direct question: 'What do you want?'

When I turn to this section of my prayer journal I like to keep these two things in mind: that I have a heavenly Father who loves me enough to shower on me undeserved gifts and that, for some reason known only to himself, my prayer releases his ability to work on my behalf so he wants me to be quite specific in my prayer for myself. This means that the prayers in the first column of this section can be quite brief and to the point. Having looked back over the past twenty-four hours in the way I have already described in the first two sections of this journal, I then look forward into the day that lies ahead and try to anticipate my needs: 'Continued inspiration for the Prayer Journal' I wrote a few days ago. 'Wisdom and inspiration for this evening's talk', I recorded a few days before that.

In the second column, I like to record a résumé of the way God answered my prayers. I find this a great booster to my faith and recommend the practice. Sometimes his answers have been so prompt and practical that I have been overwhelmed by his love. At other times I have to search my heart to try to discover what he is wanting to teach me. Sometimes I see that my request was inappropriate. Often he reminds me that some lessons can only be learned in the school of waiting. And frequently he has to remind me that my ways are not his ways; that his ways are mysterious and so much purer than my own.

I look back on this section of my Prayer Journal with thanksgiving because, more than any other, it has prompted me to echo an observation once made by Catherine Marshall: 'As we recognise our ignorance about praying aright and our helplessness, and actively seek the Spirit's help, our prayer life becomes the anteroom to amazing adventures.' [1]

My prayer is that each individual who experiments with this section of the journal will similarly sense that prayer is, indeed, an amazing adventure.

[1] *Catherine Marshall: The Helper*
Hodder and Stoughton, 1973, p.117.

'Ask and it will be given to you'

Luke 11:9

Date:

Requested:

Requesting

Received:

'Look briefly at the day ahead and beg him to be with us in every detail of it'

Gerard Hughes SJ ***God of Surprises***
DLT 1986 p.79

*'You miss what you want because you do not **ask** God for it'*

James 4:2 Moffatt

Date:

Requested:

Requesting

Received:

'Remember that the Lord walks among the pots and pans and that he will help you in the inward tasks and in the outward too'

St Teresa of Avila

'You created my inmost being; you knit me together in my mother's womb'

Psalm 139:13

Date:

Requested:

Requesting

Received:

'We only exist because God chooses to continue singing us into being'

*Ian Petit **The God Who Speaks***
DLT 1989 p.77

'Don't worry about anything, but in all your prayers ask God for what you need, always asking him with a thankful heart'

Philippans 4:6

Date:

Requested:

Requesting

Received:

'Enter my humble life with its poverty and its limitations as You entered the stable of Bethlehem, the workshop of Nazareth, the cottage of Emmaus'

Evelyn Underhill ***Meditations and Prayers***
Longmans 1949 p.20

'Your Father knows what you need before you ask him'

Matthew 6:7,8

Date:

Requested:

Requesting

Received:

'We say that we believe God to be omniscient; yet a great deal of prayer seems to consist of giving God information...We have been reminded by our Lord...not to pray as if we forgot the omniscience – for your heavenly Father knows you need all these things'

C.S. Lewis ***Letters to Malcolm***
Fount 1966 p.21

'Ask and you will receive, that your joy may be full'

John 16:24 Moffatt

Date:

Requested:

Requesting

Received:

'Asking immediately puts us into a right relationship to God. It is acting out the fact that He is the Creator with the riches and resources we need; we are the creatures who need help'

Catherine Marshall ***Adventures in Prayer***
Hodder and Stoughton 1977 p.17

'Cast all your anxiety on him because he cares for you'

1 Peter 5:7

Date:

Requested:

Requesting

Received:

'It is helpful to ask ourselves as we pray, "Do I really expect anything to happen?" This will prevent us from going window-shopping in prayer... just browsing amongst possible petitions'

Catherine Marshall ***Adventures in Prayer***
Hodder and Stoughton 1977 p.19

'This is how you should pray, "Our Father in heaven..."'

Matthew 6:9

Date:

Requested:

Requesting

Received:

'As we approach God we do so with a deep confidence that he knows what is good for us, and is constantly giving us good things in response to our praying'

Bryn Jones ***Effective Prayer***
Harvest-time 1989 p.16

'All things are possible with God'

Mark 10:27

Date:

Requested:

Requesting

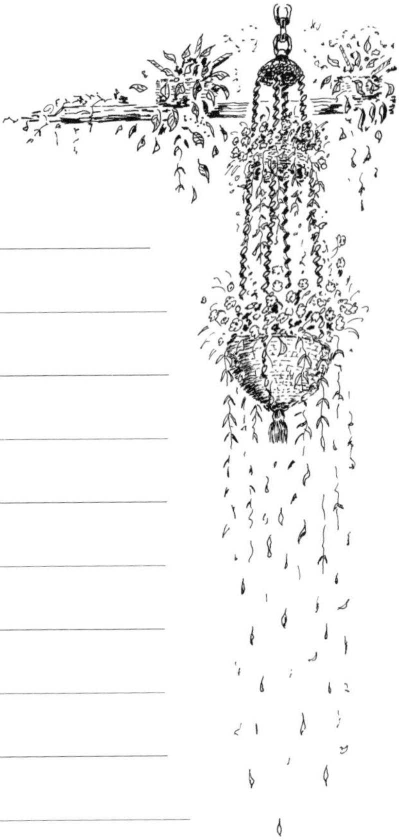

Received:

'You do not need to give detailed explanations to God of your needs, as though he is unknowing as to the pressures you are under'

Bryn Jones ***Effective Prayer***
Harvest-time 1989 p.15

Prayer For Others

Just as God wants us to pray for ourselves, so he wants us to embrace others in our prayer. Indeed, as the Holy Spirit takes us deeper and deeper into God, so he may entrust us with a burden for particular people in trouble or distress. And as we pray for such people, we may find ourselves weeping or groaning before God. Paul warns us to expect this and explains why it happens: 'We do not know what we ought to pray for, but the Spirit himself intercedes for us with groans that words cannot express' (Romans 8:26). He goes on to show that what is happening is that the Spirit is prompting us to pray 'in accordance with God's will'.

When we are being prompted to pray in this way, the situations we become prayerfully involved in may be deep and complex – not the kind where instant answers can be expected or sought. That is why I call this kind of prayer **holding prayer***. By holding prayer I simply mean that we hold the person, people or situation into the mystery of the tri-une love of the Father, the Son and the Holy Spirit. We pray as the Spirit prompts: weeping or groaning, sighing or crying, praying in tongues or whispering the Jesus Prayer: Lord Jesus Christ, Son of God, have mercy on... and, at the same time, maybe, we make a gesture such as cupping our hands to symbolise that we are holding them up to the God who alone can unravel the painful threads of complex situations.*

As I write this I am praying such a prayer. I am numb with shock at the news that my young secretary has just been killed in a car crash and I am holding to God her husband and her parents. For months now, I have been similarly holding into the love of Christ a friend who is suffering from breast cancer. At the same time, I am lifting to him two friends of mine whose marriage is crumbling, two people known to me who are suffering from burn-out, a friend who is struggling to write a book and several single friends who have asked me to pray that they may come to terms with the pain of not having married partners or the gift of children.

When praying in this way I find it helpful to write the names of such people in my Prayer Journal, to turn to this section of the notebook day by day and to intercede as the Spirit leads. Usually I find that, apart from the words of the Jesus Prayer or the mysterious language of tongues, this prayer is wordless. When I resort to words, I often find that my own distress or compassion obstructs my prayer; that I am most effective when I come before God as an empty channel through which the Spirit can pray.

But while I am interceding in this way, I do try to place myself in the shoes of the people for whom I am burdened, to look at life from their perspective and to ask God to show me whether there is anything practical I can do to alleviate their suffering. If he seems to suggest that I write a letter or send a card or show my concern in some other way, I record this in my journal so that, instead of forgetting, I am nudged into action and allow God to use me as the answer to my own prayer for those in need.

Sometimes the Spirit seems to give a burden, not for someone I know and love, but for national or international tragedies or for people in my locality who are unknown to me. I think, for example, of the taxi driver who was mugged in the town where I live. I don't know him but when I read the newspaper account of the violent assault on him, I sensed that I should hold this situation to God in prayer. So I cut from the paper the photograph and the story and stuck them into my journal. This unknown man's face stares out at me when I turn to this section of the book and reminds me to pray for him. Similarly, I have in my journal, a photograph of Terry Waite for whom I pray most days, and a map of Cyprus to remind me to hold regularly into the hands of a reconciling God an island which I love but which is still so tragically torn in two.

Because I believe that a discipline such as the one I have described can bring a healthy and necessary objectivity into our prayer life, I have labelled one section of this journal **holding prayer**. It is my hope that many users of this book will record in this section people and situations for whom they are praying; will make a note, too, of the promptings of the Spirit as they pray and stick into this section pictures and photographs, newspaper clippings or magazine articles which will persuade them to hold into the hands which created the world those for whom the Creator is asking them to pray.

'Let us love...with actions'

1 John 3:18

Date:

Person/Situation:

Prayer For Others

Prompting:

'A good letter can change the day for someone in pain, can chase away feelings of resentment, can create a smile and bring joy to the heart'

Henri Nouwen ***The Genesee Diary***
Image 1981 p.88

'I was hungry and you gave me food…I was a stranger and you made me welcome'

Matthew 25:35

Date:

Person/Situation:

Prayer For Others

Prompting:

'Love cannot be divided. If it is genuine it serves God and the neighbour in the same act. Or better, it sees God in the neighbour and the neighbour in the heart of God'

Carlo Carretto

'We should always pray and not give up'

Luke 18:1

Date:

Person/Situation:

Prayer For Others

Prompting:

'Our journal must reflect a "global consciousness", ears that hear the sobbing moan of the world's hungry, that reflect that pigs in Indiana have superior housing to a billion humans on this planet'

Richard Foster quoted in Edward England
Keeping a Spiritual Journal
Highland Books 1988 p.11

'If I…have not love, I am nothing'

1 Corinthians 13:2

Date:

Person/Situation:

Prayer For Others

Prompting:

'Lord, for the times I fail to see you in my neighbour...for the times I fail to show hospitality...have mercy'

Peter Cullen

'Love your neighbour as yourself'

Matthew 19:19

Date:

Person/Situation:

Prayer For Others

Prompting:

'What the poor need is to be wanted'

Mother Teresa of Calcutta

'Love one another as I have loved you'

John 15:12

Date:

Person/Situation:

Prayer For Others

Prompting:

'Though we do not have our Lord with us in bodily presence, we have our neighbour, who, for the ends of love and loving service, is as good as our Lord himself'

St Teresa of Avila

'Jesus...always lives to intercede for them'

Hebrews 7:25

Date:

Person/Situation:

Prayer For Others

Prompting:

'The basic meaning of intercession is not pleading with God but standing in God's presence on behalf of another. And so, simply to hold another in the silence before God, may become for us the most important way of intercessory prayer'

Robert Llewellyn ***Prayer and Contemplation***
SLG Press 1975 p.13

Prayer Jottings

Some people, I imagine, will use this journal daily. Others may use it weekly. And yet others may keep it for special occasions like Quiet Days or retreats. But the art of using it will be similar on each occasion. We look back and say thank you to God for some of his many gifts and ask him to show us where the Holy Spirit has been working on us as a potter re-shaping clay. And we look forward, admitting our helplessness and powerlessness; our need of him.

The second section of the journal may make us marvel as God gives us glimpses of the ways in which we are being changed into his likeness. At such times we may want to express our feelings to him in a prayer. At other times, when God brings us face to face with our failure, we may find ourselves wanting to pour out our grief and sorrow; to confess. This section of the journal has been reserved for such prayers.

In it, too, we may want to store the special insights which have come to us as we have meditated on the Bible. Or we may want to record particular verses from our Scripture reading which have attracted us to themselves for some reason. This is also a good place to copy out quotations from books which have comforted or challenged or provoked us. I also keep, in this section of my journal, the notes I have made during talks and sermons which have inspired me.

In other words, this part of the journal is a place for recording prayer jottings where we write to God and he writes to us.

And by the time this book has been filled up, you will have discovered whether the discipline of journalling is of value to you on your prayer journey or not. If it helps you draw closer to God, continue to use it. All you need is a notebook or a loose-leaf file with four sections: one for recording your thanks, another to show you where your life revolves around you and where it revolves around God, a third to record your requests and a fourth which will become a spiritual scrapbook to be treasured by you and God.

'We do not know what we ought to pray for, but…the Spirit helps us in our weakness'

Romans 8:26

'The first lesson we have to learn about prayer…is that it is God's activity in us and not a self-activated process of our own'

Mother Mary Clare SLG ***Learning to Pray***
SLG Press No.12 p.5

'His love is eternal'

Psalm 106:1

Date:

Prayer Jottings

'The most important thing that happens between God and the human soul is to love and be loved'

Kallistos Kataphygiotis
14c

'As the deer pants for streams of water, so my soul pants for you, O God'

Psalm 42:1

Date:

Prayer Jottings

'Thirst after Jesus and he will satisfy you with his love'

St Isaac the Syrian
7c

'Be still, and know that I am God'

Psalm 46:10

Date:

Prayer Jottings

'Unless there is a centre in the middle of the storm, unless a man in the midst of all his activities preserves a secret room in his heart where he stands alone before God, then he will lose all sense of spiritual direction and be torn to pieces'

Kallistos Ware

'In stillness and in staying quiet, there lies your strength'

Isaiah 30:15

Date:

Prayer Jottings

'Our ministries…must flow from prayer and lead people back to prayer, for it is in prayer that we experience our personal love relationship with Jesus'

*John Michael Talbot **The Lover and the Beloved** Marshall Pickering 1985 p.86*

'I will lead her into the desert and speak tenderly to her'

Hosea 1:14

Date:

Prayer Jottings

'We need to find God and he cannot be found in noise and restlessness. God is the friend of silence'

Mother Teresa of Calcutta

'I have stilled and quietened my soul, like a weaned child with its mother, like a weaned child is my soul within me'

Psalm 131:2

Date:

Prayer Jottings

'In God I feel like a child in its mother's lap'

Carlo Carretto ***Love is for Living***
DLT 1976 p.19

'The Lord would speak to Moses face to face, as a man speaks with his friend'

Exodus 32:11

Date:

Prayer Jottings

'Christians believe in a God who ***speaks.*** *Ours is not a silent God, a God who sits Sphynx-like, looking out unblinking on a world in agony'*

Donald Coggan ***The Sacrament of the Word***
Fount 1987 p.31

'I have called you by name, you are mine'

Isaiah 43:1

Date:

Prayer Jottings

'You called me and your cry overcame my deafness, you shone out and your light overcame my blindness; you surrounded me with your fragrance and I breathed it in, so that now I yearn for more of you'

St Augustine

'As one whom his mother comforts, so I will comfort you'

Isaiah 66:13

Date:

Prayer Jottings

'Do not be afraid to throw yourself on the Lord! He will not draw back and let you fall! Put your worries aside and throw yourself on him. He will welcome you and heal you'

St Augustine

'Speak, Lord, for your servant is listening'

1 Samuel 3:9

Date:

Prayer Jottings

'God often talks to us directly in Scripture. That is, He plants the words full of actual graces as we read them and sudden undiscovered meanings are sown in our hearts, if we attend to them, reading with minds that are at prayer'

Thomas Merton ***The Seven Storey Mountain***
Sheldon Press 1975 pp.293-294

'When you pray, go into your room and close the door'

Matthew 6:6

Date:

Prayer Jottings

'Has it ever occurred to you that Jesus, that master in the art of prayer, would take the trouble to walk up a hill in order to pray? Like all great contemplatives he was aware that the place in which we pray has an influence on the quality of our prayer'

Anthony de Mello SJ ***Sadhana***
Gujarat Sahitya Prakash Anand India 1979 p.62

Jesus said, "I am the Bread of Life"'

John 6:35

Date:

Prayer Jottings

'Prayer is rather like chewing the cud: you take a little and you stay with it until you have drained out all the goodness – not all the goodness that will ever be got out, but all that is there for you for the time being'

Margaret Hebblethwaite ***Finding God in All Things***
Fount 1987 p.49

'He brought me to the banqueting house, and his banner over me was love'

Song of Solomon 2:5

Date:

Prayer Jottings

'Prayer is essentially a love affair with God'

Mother Mary Clare SLG ***Learning to Pray***
SLG Press No.12 p.10

'I am my beloved's and his desire is for me'

Song of Solomon 7:1

Date:

Prayer Jottings

'The language which God best hears
is the silent language of love'

St John of the Cross.